Sylvie K...

Born to be Queen

Illustrated by Barry Glynn

PENGUIN BOOKS
in association with

PRIVATE EYE

Penguin Books Ltd, Harmondsworth, Middlesex, England
Penguin Books, 625 Madison Avenue, New York, New York, 10022, U.S.A.
Penguin Books Australia Ltd, Ringwood, Victoria, Australia
Penguin Books Canada Ltd, 2801 John Street, Markham, Ontario, Canada L3R 1B4
Penguin Books (N.Z.) Ltd, 182-190 Wairau Road, Auckland 10, New Zealand

First published in *Private Eye* 1980-81
Published in Penguin Books 1981

Made and printed in Great Britain by
Hazell, Watson and Viney Ltd, Aylesbury
Set in Palatino

♛ *Chapter 1* ♛

The story so far: His Royal Highness Prince Charles is still unmarried at the age of thirty-two.

Searching for a suitable bride, his eye lights on lovely nineteen-year-old Lady Diana Spencer.

LADY DARTMOUTH's hands trembled slightly as she picked up the large cream envelope embossed with the Royal Crest which lay on top of her silver breakfast tray.

'What's that you've got there, darling?' came the commanding voice of her mother, the gracious authoress Dame Barbara Cartland, who sat at the far end of the table swathed in furs and surrounded by pots of honey and vitamin pills. No wonder, her daughter thought, that even at eighty-four she still made men's heads turn when she shopped for yoghurt in Harrods.

Lady Dartmouth ran a silver paperknife through the hand-made envelope. Her voice trembling with emotion she read aloud: 'His Royal Highness the Prince Charles requests the pleasure of Lady Diana Spencer at Windsor Castle November 29th. Polo and free-fall parachuting. Black tie.'

At that moment the door opened, and four sleek black labradors bounded into the breakfast room followed by the Earl of Spencer wearing his customary smart tweeds and green wellington boots.

'What's up, darling?' he cried, helping himself to kedgeree at the sideboard.

Lady Dartmouth gave her husband a despairing look.

'If you must know,' she said in icy tones, 'your daughter has received an invitation from the Palace. You realize what *that* might mean.'

The Earl took his place at the table and sprinkled royal jelly absent-mindedly on his plate. Sometimes he wished he had never agreed to marry Raine. She could be so overbearing. And as for her mother, now firmly established in the spare wing, there were moments when he thought she was a terrible ogre out of a fairy-tale.

His reverie was interrupted by the brush of young lips on his cheek.

'Good morning, papa!' came the soft reassuring voice of his daughter Diana.

'Never mind that, you silly child!' her stepmother rasped. 'Look at this! An invitation from the Prince of Wales. You've to spend a weekend with him at Windsor November 29th.'

The innocent young Diana blushed.

'But Raine! That's the weekend of the Young Farmers' Ball! I promised to help with the Tombola.'

Now it was her step-grandmother's turn to interrupt.

'Fiddlesticks, child!' came her powerful ringing tones from the end of the table. 'Don't you realize what your mother is telling you? The future King of England is inviting you to his home. If he should take a shine to you, well . . . surely you don't need me to tell you what this could do for your mother and me!'

The old earl could see the disappointment and confusion in Diana's beautiful young face. Her large doe-like eyes filled with tears.

The Prince of Wales, she thought. She had seen his somewhat gawky figure at parties. They had exchanged a few words.

Certainly he dressed smartly and was well groomed as might be expected. But there was nothing special in his conversation.

And what was it her stepmother had called him – 'a man of the world'? What did she mean by that? Even at school, she remembered, there had been stories about him in the gossip columns. A series of girls whose names had been linked with his.

What type of man was it who seemed to give his favours so freely – even, it had been whispered, to married women of low birth?

But then, perhaps, it was traditional for kings of England to behave in that sort of way. She had seen the TV series called 'Edward and Mrs Simpson'.

'Well, that's agreed then,' said her stepmother firmly, refilling her Meissen coffee cup. 'You will write at once to the Young Farmers. And then we have a very busy day ahead of us. Mumsy, be an angel and ring Marcel. Her hair is a perfect mess. And George, you've got nothing to do. You can take us to the station. She can't be seen dead in any of those clothes she wears. We'll go up to town and get you a nice sensible outfit from Mr Hartnell. This is your big chance, Diana. And you won't get anywhere unless you look your best.'

Diana gazed out at the bleak November Northamptonshire countryside. The bare black trees and the grey sky seemed to echo the mood of her heart.

👑 *Chapter 2* 👑

*In which Lady Diana dines for the first time at Windsor Castle.
'Diana could not but feel she was being put to some test . . .'*

'THIS IS your room, Your Ladyship,' the Royal Equerry announced solemnly, ushering the petite Diana into the sumptuous Queen Victoria Suite in Windsor Castle.

'You'll find everything you need. There will be a bell for dinner. Her Majesty likes her guests to be punctual. His Royal Highness asks if you will be good enough to join him for a cocktail in half an hour in the Smoking Room.'

Diana gazed about her as the door closed. What a hectic week it had been!

That silly Norman Hartnell making such a fuss! And what a hideous dress her stepmother had chosen for her – flamingo-pink satin with a feather bodice.

She looked at her watch and sighed. There would be just enough time to bathe and change. She unzipped her overnight case and saw to her surprise, lying on top of her carefully folded nightdress, a book which she did not remember packing – *Etiquette for Young Gentlewomen* by Barbara Cartland!

Was there nowhere she could be free from the overpowering presence of her step-grandmother?

👑   👑   👑

'Well, you made it, did you?' said the Prince, pouring himself a Cinzano Bianco from a silver decanter. 'Are you sure you won't have anything?'

Diana felt herself blushing as she sat uncomfortably on the edge of a Louis Quatorze chaise-longue.

'No thank you, Sir,' she murmured. Was that the correct way to address him? She couldn't remember what her step-grandmother had written.

'I say! Come off it!' beamed the Prince. 'Call me Charles. Or better still, Charlie. I am a bit of a Charlie, don't you think? That's what all my friends say.'

He laughed, revealing a fine set of gleaming teeth. She noticed his ears for the first time. Jug-handles, they called them at school.

The Prince took his drink and sat down next to her.

'If you don't drink, what are your vices, eh?' he smiled, nudging her rather suggestively in the ribs.

She felt herself beginning to blush again. But then, to her relief, the phone rang. The Prince crossed the room and picked up the receiver.

'Hullo?' he cried. 'Who? Hello, Lavinia! How goes it? Oh, he's away, is he? Supper tonight? No, it's a bit awkward. How about Thursday? Fine. Bye!'

She had been trying not to listen. But it was difficult to ignore what had clearly been the shrill voice of an eager young woman at the other end of the line.

As the Prince replaced the receiver, the large oak door burst open and the Duke of Edinburgh, dressed for dinner as an Admiral of the Fleet, strode in.

'Hullo Charlie! At it again, what?' he beamed, giving Diana a broad wink. 'Which one are you, then? Of course, you're George Spencer's gel, the one we all ... um ... er ... what?'

His voice trailed away as he caught sight of his wife who had entered silently and was signalling to him from the doorway.

'Poor old George!' mused the Duke, kicking aside an intrusive corgi. 'Fancy having the Dartmouth harpie around his neck! And as for that Cartland woman!'

A gong sounded, drowning the Duke's laughter, and they went in to dinner.

Dinner was an awkward affair. The Duke, she noticed, drank heavily while Her Majesty eyed her silently from the far end of the table.

Charles on the other hand seemed perfectly happy, doing impressions of Spike Milligan and regaling them with stories from the polo field.

She noticed how twice during the meal he was called away to the telephone, returning on both occasions flushed and obviously well pleased with himself.

Somewhere a clock struck midnight. It had been an arduous evening and Diana could not but feel that she was being put to some test.

She was about to get undressed when there was a loud knock at her door. Her heart leapt in her beautiful young throat. Surely this could not be – the unthinkable?

'Who's there?' Her voice was a whisper.

And then the Duke burst in, his face flushed and his medals askew. 'What ho!' he cried. 'Sorry to barge in. Unearthly hour. Word in your ear.' He sat down clumsily on the edge of her bed, his head bent forward.

'Now look here!' he began. 'You've probably twigged what we're up to. You're a sensible young girl by the look of you.'

Whatever the Duke was trying to say, he wasn't finding it easy.

'Our people have vetted you pretty thoroughly. No lunacy in the family. Everything hunky-dory. Now you just keep your nose clean, alright? And whatever you do, don't go talking to the press. That could sink the whole thing. See you on Church Parade, 1100 hours.'

Then he was gone, as abruptly as he had come. Diana undressed and climbed into bed. But she couldn't sleep. Her mind was swimming with the Duke's ominous phrases.

And then there was the telephone bell that seemed to ring incessantly throughout the night ...

♕ *Chapter 3* ♕

In which a Royal Visitor arrives at Althorp.
"'Delightful girl, sweet-natured and exquisite manners . . .'"

THE NORTHAMPTONSHIRE sky was heavy with snow. The old oaks that dotted the rolling lawns looked black and ominous, their branches smudged against the late afternoon skyline.

Lady Diana Spencer turned her beautiful doe-like eyes from the chilly prospect and gazed at her step-grandmother, Barbara Cartland, ensconced by the blazing log-fire and surrounded by her favourite Pekinese, Chi-Chi and Yo-Ko.

Opposite sat her stepmother, Raine. She was reading again the letter from Windsor Castle which had followed Diana's short stay there two weeks before.

Lady Dartmouth had read it to her so many times that she could almost recite it by heart.

'Delightful girl, sweet-natured and exquisite manners . . . our fondest hope that our two families will be drawn even closer . . .'

Since the arrival of the Queen's letter, life at Althorp had become almost unbearable.

Dame Barbara Cartland in particular had not lost a single opportunity to criticize her slightest faults.

'Don't draw the curtains, child,' she cried even now. 'A future Queen of England should leave that kind of thing to the servants!'

How her life had changed! It seemed only yesterday that her real mother had sat in that very chair, reading the Christmas issue of *Country Life* and talking about skiing in Gstaad.

But now her family could speak of nothing except her impending marriage to Prince Charles – a man she hardly knew: a man who, if the newspapers were to be believed, was a Royal Romeo, and little short of a cad.

But Raine Dartmouth, as Diana had learned to her dismay, was not a woman to be crossed. Not for nothing had she single-handedly prevented the demolition of half of London!

Suddenly the old oak doors swung open and her father, the Duke of Spencer, tottered in with a brace of pheasants in one hand and a shotgun under his arm.

Raine viewed him scornfully from her chaise-longue.

'George!' she cried. 'How many times must I tell you not to walk on the carpet with your dirty wellingtons – and get those dogs out of here! You know how much they irritate little Chi-Chi and Yo-Ko!'

The Duke, looking crestfallen, shooed the dogs out of the room.

'By the way,' he mumbled as he turned to go. 'Almost forgot. There's some young man hovering about in the portico. Short chap with big ears; looks familiar but I couldn't place him.'

As the Duke spoke, Old Wapping, the butler, pushed past him, cleared his throat and announced: 'His Royal Highness the Prince Charles for Lady Diana – if it please you, Ma'am!'

'*J*ust passing by on my way to the Hunt Ball. Thought I'd drop in.' Prince Charles paused before a family portrait of the 3rd Earl on the first-floor landing. It had been Raine's suggestion that Diana should show their Royal visitor the family heirlooms upstairs.

She mumbled something. She was not quite sure what to say. His presence made her uncomfortable. He seemed so much older, with his jokes and wandering hands, reminding her at times of her father's shooting friends.

Even now he had taken her arm and seemed to be steering her towards the bedroom.

'And what have you got locked away in here, eh?' he beamed.

Before she knew what was happening she was alone in the sanctity of her room and the future King of England was breathing hotly on her alabaster cheek.

'You're a pretty little thing and no mistake,' he was saying.

And then panic seized her. She was running out of the room, down the huge marble stairway, past row upon row of Spencers, past her step-grandmother immortalized for ever by the brushes of Signor Annigoni . . .

Away, away, out into the dark! Out into the first of winter's snow. But as she ran, she knew in her heart she would be called back, and there would be no escape . . .

👑 *Chapter 4* 👑

In which some cards are laid on the table.
'"Good Lord, boy! Surely it's obvious . . ."'

'COME IN, my boy, and sit down.' The Duke of Edinburgh, wearing his informal Field Marshal's uniform, motioned his eldest son Prince Charles to enter the Library at Sandringham.

Charles made his way across the priceless Ferguskhashin carpet towards the fire where his father was standing, arms akimbo in his familiar nautical posture.

Her Majesty The Queen, her spectacles neatly perched on her nose, sat demurely on the edge of a sofa, apparently intent on her embroidery.

'Now then,' the Duke began. 'The reason your mother and I have sent for you is perfectly simple. Just look out there.'

The young man strolled confidently to the high French windows, pulled back the drapes and stared out at the scene.

The herbaceous borders, now bearing a white mantle of snow, stretched away towards the high north wall which marked the boundary of the estate.

There, perched on the ancient brickwork, could be seen rank upon rank of press photographers, with their expensive lenses trained on the very room where they now sat.

In the park beyond he could see caravans and tents, mobile catering facilities and hundreds of milling journalists struggling to gain a point of vantage on the wall.

'I don't get it,' said the young Prince, averting his gaze from the unpleasing spectacle. 'They're not there because of Great-Aunt Alice, surely?'

'Don't be so bloody wet!' snapped the Duke. 'It's you and that Spencer gel that they're after. You ask your mother, she'll tell you.'

The Queen looked up from her embroidery with a worried frown.

'We do find it rather tiresome, darling,' she began, taking a handkerchief and delicately blowing her nose. 'They're such a rough collection. Yesterday at the Gymkhana one of them jumped out of the bushes and made poor Peter's pony bolt. The little boy was terrified!'

'Quite, quite!' the Duke grunted irritably. 'But the reason we're here is simply this. There's only one way of getting rid of that rabble outside, and that's for you to tell them what they want to know.'

The Prince sat down at his mother's writing desk and absently toyed with an ormolu letter-opener.

'Don't get, pater,' he said at last. 'Tell them what?'

His father thumped his forehead with the flat of his hand in a display of exasperation.

'Good lord, boy!' he rasped through clenched teeth. 'Surely it's obvious . . .'

Her Majesty put down her embroidery and gazed firmly at her son.

'What your father is saying is that as soon as you announce that you are going to marry Diana Spencer the interest will quickly fade and we will be able to continue our lives in relative peace.'

'Precisely!' echoed the Duke. 'That's it in a nutshell. Your mother and I have talked it over. We're quite prepared to play our part, even if it means having that dreadful Cartland baggage hanging around our necks for the rest of our lives, not to mention the Dartmouth woman . . .'

Charles got up and poured himself a drink under the disapproving gaze of his mother.

'But, I say,' he stammered awkwardly. 'Don't jump the gun. I mean, I haven't even yet ... you know ...'

The Duke did not wait for him to finish his sentence.

'Well the sooner you get it over with,' he snapped, 'the better it'll be for all of us. You're thirty-two now. You've had your bit of fun. Now's the time to pop the question. And that's an order, my boy!'

'Yes, Sir!' Charles clicked his heels automatically and saluted. As he did so the telephone rang. The Duke picked up the receiver.

'Who? Lavinia who?' The Duke stared into his son's eyes.

'No, I'm afraid he isn't here. He's otherwise ... engaged. Goodbye.'

As the Duke replaced the receiver the three of them stood silently in the January twilight. The only sound was the distant shouting and laughter of the newsmen and photographers as they prepared for another nocturnal vigil in the snow-covered fields.

👑  👑

In which the gentlemen of the Press make their presence felt.
'Diana felt the fresh wind on her soft damask cheeks . . .'

IT WAS a clear frosty morning in early January. Outside the Battenburg Arms in the little Norfolk village of Sandringham the Royal Hunt was gathered in all its glory. A hundred pedigree hounds sniffed the air expectantly, as stewards handed up tiny crystal goblets of piping hot cherry brandy to the mounted huntsmen – elegantly dressed gentlemen in pink frocks, beautiful svelte ladies in tight-fitting velveteen hacking jackets.

And at the centre of it all, the couple on whom the eyes of the world were focused: Charles and Diana, as they were beginning to be known to their friends – he resplendent on a magnificent Viennese stallion; she demure and enchanting on her own thoroughbred mare, Cartland II.

Only one thing marred the picture-postcard setting of the scene – the group of tousle-haired, pasty-faced journalists in their grubby sheepskin coats lurking in the churchyard on the far side of the village green, their cameras clicking and flashing like a thousand glow-worms in the tropical night.

Suddenly the bugle sounded 'Tally-ho!' and hounds and huntsmen set off down Wheatcroft Lane at a slow canter.

Lady Diana was grateful to be on the move at last. She was looking forward to a day in the saddle, free for a short while at least from the prying eyes of the newsmen.

But, to her dismay, no sooner had they drawn close to the churchyard than Charles began to wave at them in a friendly fashion, crying 'Good morning, gentlemen! Why, you are up early, 'pon my soul!'

Delighted by this greeting, the pressmen cheered and laughed in response.

'Got your leg over yet, Charlie?' shouted one red-faced little Scotsman, brandishing a copy of the *Daily Mirror*.

Instead of ignoring him, as Diana hoped he would, His Royal Highness gave the man a broad wink as he dug his heels into his horse's flanks and sped off towards Chancellor's Copse.

👑　　　👑　　　👑

*A*t last they were in the open country, away from everything and everyone. Speeding across the sward, Diana felt the fresh wind on her soft damask cheeks. Then, suddenly, as they cantered together down a grassy knoll, Charles leaned towards her and whispered, 'I say, old girl. There's something important I've just got to tell you. But not here. I know of a little spot – just the other side of the wood. An old barn, where we can be alone.'

Diana blushed. What could he mean? She felt a sense of foreboding. Again the stories of the gutter press flashed through her mind and she remembered his hot wandering hands in her bedroom at Althorp . . .

But obediently she followed his suggestion. Charles had by now deliberately fallen behind the other riders and they were alone as they picked their way along the rutted track to a dark wooden building on the corner of the wood . . .

Charles tethered the horses to a sapling and beckoned Lady Diana into the dark musty interior of the barn.

'It's alright,' he reassured her, taking her hand. 'There's no need to be frightened.'

She felt her heart pounding as the Heir to the Throne led her towards a pile of hay which filled the back of the building.

'Sit down,' he said with a genial smile. 'Care for a snifter? I've got something here.'

And he withdrew a gleaming silver hipflask from his jodhpur pocket.

Lady Diana politely declined. But Charles put the hipflask to his lips and took a long deep draught.

'Now then,' he began, smacking his lips. 'About that little matter I mentioned. You've probably guessed what it's about. You see, it's this way . . .'

He had taken a step towards her when the silence of the barn was broken by a loud cry from above in a rich Scottish brogue:

'Go on, Jimmy, give her one!'

And then a rafter gave way with an ear-splitting crack, and the rotund

figure of the Scottish journalist she had seen outside the church crashed
down into the hay, his cameras bouncing about his corpulent frame.

'Great powers, McKay!' cried the Prince. 'Is there nowhere where we can
be free of you?'

Trembling with emotion, Diana jumped up and ran from the barn. How
terrible that this grubby newsman had witnessed their intimate tête-à-tête!

And yet, after all, she thought, what a blessing! For who could tell what the
future King of England had had in store for her?

Chapter 6

*In which another attempt is made to lay cards on the table.
'He did not relish the task before him . . .'*

IT WAS market day in the little Northamptonshire town of Melford Stevenson. Crowds of ruddy-faced farmers jostled with shopping house-wives in the narrow streets.

Dame Barbara Cartland and her stepdaughter Lady Raine Dartmouth made it a habit to motor into Melford every Thursday to do their shopping and afterwards lunch together at the Harold Krishna health food emporium in a quiet backstreet.

'It's all very unsatisfactory, darling,' Dame Barbara began, pouring a spoonful of Tasmanian honey over her seaweed steak. 'It's been a month today since Sandringham and still no announcement. What can that stepdaughter of yours be doing?'

Lady Dartmouth sipped her viper's-bugloss tea nervously.

'It's no good getting cross, Mummy,' she said. 'You know what young people are like today. They simply won't make up their minds.'

'Fiddlesticks!' cried the Dame, as an elderly waitress wearing saffron robes laid a plateful of oatmeal truffles in front of her. 'Prince Charles, I feel sure, has behaved like a perfect gentleman. His intentions are absolutely honourable. That gel of yours is just a little flippertigibbet who needs a good spanking, if you ask me!'

'Sssh, Mummy!' hissed Raine Dartmouth. 'The people at the next table are looking at you!'

'So what if they are?' said the unrepentant Dame. 'It's high time matters were brought to a head. If you won't do anything, then it's up to George! He is the girl's father, goodness knows!'

And with that the Dame, resplendent in her ostrich-feathered hat, rose to her feet and strode to the counter, her daughter trailing behind her.

'It's not as if he's got anything else to do,' she persisted as she piled her weekly supply of vitamin pills, ginseng tablets, Bulgarian yoghurt and nut rissoles into her bulging string-bag. 'All he ever does is mope around the house getting in everyone's way!'

And so she continued throughout the afternoon.

George Spencer hung his hat up and lovingly replaced his trusty Oswald Hickson twelve-bore in its pinewood case. He kicked off his wellingtons, absent-mindedly picked up a carton of what looked like Bulgarian yoghurt from the string-bag that someone had left on the gunroom table and poured the contents into the dogbowl.

Then he whistled to his trusty retrievers Goodman and Derrick to 'come fetch'.

He did not relish the task before him. His wife's shrill tones still echoed in his heavy heart – 'It's a man's job, George! If you don't talk to her now, this golden opportunity will slip forever through our fingers!'

Dash it! he thought. What was this 'golden opportunity' his wife kept on about? Diana married to the King of England! He could see it all. An endless succession of official functions – dinners, church services, photographers everywhere. Why, it was bad enough having to chair the parish council meeting twice a year.

He sighed and poured himself a long stiff Scotch from a crystal decanter. A clock struck four. Diana would be waiting for him in the library.

And so it turned out. She looked as beautiful as ever, her golden blonde hair framing her youthful peachlike complexion in the soft glow of the firelight.

'Hullo, Daddy!' she cried, running towards him and throwing her arms round his neck. 'Did you have a nice walk? Mummy said you wanted to see me.'

George Spencer sighed again and sat down in the worn leather Parker-Bowles chair by the fire. He took a spotted handkerchief from his pocket and mopped his brow.

'Is there something wrong, Daddy?' Lady Diana asked, her limpid blue eyes creased with filial concern.

The old Earl lifted his head and looked lovingly at his only daughter.

She was too good for that randy young good-for-nothing, he thought. And yet here he was, about to urge her to accept his hand.

'What was it, Daddy?' she persisted. 'What you wanted to ask me?'

'Oh . . .' stuttered the Earl. 'Oh, that! Yes. I know. I wanted to ask you what you would like for your birthday, that's all.'

She laughed, and suddenly the room seemed filled with the tinkling of a mountain stream.

'Silly old daddy!' she cried. 'You know I'll love anything you choose!'

And with that she turned and skipped from the room.

Then the Earl heard the footsteps of his wife on the old back stairway. It was time to face the music again.

♛ *Chapter 7* ♛

In which old ties are severed.
  'She knew with her woman's intuition that he had something on his mind . . .'

VENETIA BARKWORTH-SMYTHE stood alone in the morning room of Piggott's Lodge, the lavish Berkshire home where she and her racehorse-trainer husband, Derek, had lived for fifteen years.

She was an elegant woman with long raven hair that tumbled in open waves over her svelte well-formed shoulders.

Her soft limpid eyes strayed to the French windows just across the frosty lawn and to where a bright red Lamborghini was discreetly parked under a cypress tree.

The ormolu clock behind her struck eleven. The Prince was cutting it a bit fine, she thought. Derek's plane was due into Heathrow in an hour's time. He would be in Hungerford by two.

Then the door behind her opened and His Royal Highness Prince Charles, looking spruce and well-groomed in his check sports jacket, strode purposefully into the bright sunny room.

'Morning, Venetia,' he beamed, pouring himself a large cup of black coffee and joining her by the window. 'Beautiful day isn't it? It's incredible, I've just . . . I mean, I've often wished I could paint.'

Venetia Barkworth-Smythe smiled reassuringly. 'You do so many other things so well, Charles,' she said.

The Prince sipped his coffee. There was an awkward silence. She knew with her woman's intuition that he had something on his mind.

'Ahem!' coughed the Prince. 'There's something I think I ought to tell you . . . Shall we sit down?'

They walked together to a pair of chintz-covered easy chairs and sat down facing each other. She crossed her long legs and leaned forward. 'Let me make it easy for you, your Royal Highness,' she soothed. 'You're trying to tell me that you are planning to marry – and that it will mean an end to our happy times here together.'

The Prince fidgeted nervously and began to fiddle with the knot in his tie.

'Let me say if I may, your Majesty,' she intervened, 'that I entirely understand. You will not find me one of those women to nurse a grudge or display jealousy. And I will always treasure the memory of our wonderful times together.'

She rose, and planted a chaste kiss on his forehead.

♕   ♕   ♕

Charles steered the Lamborghini expertly through the winding Berkshire lanes.

The keen February wind whistled around his ears, bringing a flush to his manly cheeks.

What a relief, he thought! With her exquisite tact Mrs Barkworth-Smythe had said it all. The unpleasantness that he half expected had been mercifully averted.

Yes, he was exhilarated. With his foot hard down on the throttle his powerful machine thundered down the fast lane of the M4. Huge juggernauts pulled over to one side as the laughing Prince flashed his lights and hooted, while the police, recognizing the Royal number plate, waved him on with friendly smiles.

Yes, it was high time he severed his links with Venetia once and for all. This would be the last time he would make the journey to Hungerford.

Was there a tinge of sadness? Perhaps. After all, Venetia had been good to him. A woman of the world, she had taught him the ways to please a woman. For this alone he would owe her an eternal debt of gratitude.

As from today he would knuckle down to his Royal duties. Diana would be at his side, her innocent young eyes gazing at him in rapt adoration.

That was to be it from now on. That was what his parents wished. Even now, elaborate plans were being drawn up for what newsmen were already calling the Wedding of the Century.

But, as he pulled off the motorway to Windsor, a dark cloud of foreboding began to loom over his air of resolution. A married man. Duties to the throne. Pomp and circumstance.

He drove his car into the courtyard and a Beefeater immediately stepped forward to take his bags.

The Prince strode swiftly towards the library where he knew he could be alone. 'Bring me a drink, Wheatcroft,' he cried to the Beefeater. 'A large brandy. And be quick about it!'

He had promised to phone Diana to make arrangements for the Australian trip and, because of the weekend, it had gone clean out of his mind. Damn! That would mean the wretched Cartland woman would be ringing up his mother to complain. The old virago never missed an opportunity of speaking direct to the Royalty.

He crossed the library floor to the ornate enamelled telephone, a present from King Otto of Bavaria to Queen Victoria, and took out his address book.

Lady Diana? Where would she be? He could try the flat, but that might mean talking to one of those half-witted giggling girls she shared with.

The book fell open under B, and his eye somehow focused immediately on the name of Barkworth-Smythe.

As if in a trance he found himself dialling the familiar Hungerford number. Brr! Brr!, Brr! Brr! Already the words were forming in his mind – 'Venetia, I've been thinking over what we were saying this morning. I don't think we ought to rush to any conclusions about us . . .'

There was a click at the other end of the line. 'Hello? Hello? Derek Barkworth-Smythe speaking – who is this?'

The Prince replaced the receiver with an oath. Damn! Damn! Damn!

👑 *Chapter 8* 👑

In which an Invitation is received.
'Already she could see the crowded Cathedral . . .'

WINDSOR CASTLE was a hive of activity. Ever since the announcement of the engagement between Charles and Diana, there had been a non-stop flow of visitors, telephone calls and, of course, sacks of telegrams and letters. All bore the same good wishes.

Now the young Prince wandered aimlessly down the long corridors, twirling a polo stick from side to side.

It had all been so sudden. The unexpected meeting at Buckingham Palace when he and Diana had been told in no uncertain terms by the Queen and the Duke that they were to announce their engagement the following day.

Failure to do so, the Queen said, could well mean a six-year stint as Governor-General of the Falkland Islands with no leave.

The Prince shuddered at the thought even now.

As he passed the massive door of the Huw Wheldon Library, the Duke emerged, wearing his Air Vice-Marshal's uniform.

'Come in, sonny!' he beckoned. 'Your mother and I want a word with you.'

Charles obeyed at once and entered the long book-lined room at the far end of which he could just discern the bespectacled figure of his mother, seated beside a huge replica of St Paul's Cathedral with the roof off.

'What's up, Mein Kapitan?' asked the Prince in his Goon Show voice.

'Cut that out, Charles!' said his father. 'You can save that kind of thing for your stag party.'

Together they walked briskly down the magnificent Ferguskhashin carpet to the Queen's dais.

His mother, Charles noted, was in one of her iciest moods. He had hoped that the announcement of his forthcoming marriage would have softened her attitude towards him. But, if anything, she seemed more aloof.

At the side of her throne stood a large tea-chest filled with tiny plastic figurines, each one bearing a name neatly sellotaped to its base.

'So much for Mrs Thatcher and the Cabinet,' Her Majesty said, turning to the equerry at her side, who took the figurines and placed them in the model.

'Well,' continued the Queen imperiously, 'we have done our side of the Cathedral. After luncheon we will deal with the Spencers. I expect you to be here, Charles, and to show a little more interest in the seating plan. It is after all *your* wedding that we are discussing.'

And with that she rose and swept out past the line of bowing servants.

Mornings for Dame Barbara Cartland were something of a ritual. Ever since she could remember, she rose promptly at six-thirty, did half an hour of physical training in her leotard and then sat down to breakfast – which consisted always of a bowl of live Latvian yoghurt, two ounces of Gunga nuts from the Valley of the Rajneesh, and assorted vitamin pills, yeast tablets and the like.

Then, surrounded by her faithful Pekinese dogs and swathed in her celebrated feather boa, she would dictate an entire novel before elevenses.

But today, no sooner had she settled down to Chapter One of *The Admiral and the Gypsy Girl* than the door of her suite burst open and her daughter Raine rushed into the room, holding a gold-embossed envelope.

'Mumsy darling!' she cried, smothering the Dame's carefully powdered face with kisses. 'Stop whatever you're doing! It's here! It's here!'

'What, child?' shrilled Dame Barbara, switching off her dictaphone.

'Why, the invitation, of course! Isn't it exciting!'

'Give it to me!' snapped the old crone, grabbing the envelope and ripping it open with trembling fingers.

Already she could see the crowded Cathedral. The flags. The choir. The mighty organ. Charles and Diana kneeling at the high altar before the kindly white-haired figure of Archbishop Runcieballs. And there, as the cameras whirred, taking the picture to every far-flung corner of the universe – herself, resplendent in her mother's diamond tiara. And wasn't that The Queen at her side, asking if she could borrow a hankie for a moment to wipe the tears from her cheek.

Adjusting her lorgnette, she read the card. Then, with a terrifying scream, the ancient beldame fell to the floor, flattening her faithful Pekinese Woy beneath her.

'Mumsy, mumsy, what's the matter?' cried Raine, bending down and picking up the card.

Then, as she read, she understood:

Her Majesty the Queen
and HRH the Duke of Edinburgh
request the pleasure of the company
of Dame Barbara Cartland
at the wedding of
their son Charles
in Westminster Abbey

Your seat number is
Row Z No 47
(NB: *RESTRICTED VIEW*)
Please bring this card with you.

👑 *Chapter 9* 👑

In which pride comes before a fall.
'He felt his heart pounding with excitement . . .'

IT WAS a glorious early spring day at Melford Stevenson – the day of the Lord Whelks Three Mile Novices Steeplechase Handicap.

The bright sun shone on the paddock, lighting up the gay glittering colours of the jockeys like an aquarium of tropical fish.

Everyone was there. The Queen's own trainer Lord Dorchester chatted respectfully with Dame Barbara Cartland, resplendent as always in her magnificent feather boa, her Pekinese gambolling playfully about her ankles.

And there at the bar, the graceful figure of Her Royal Highness Princess Margaret shared a joke with the rubicund Earl George Spencer himself, wearing his old plus-fours and carrying a venerable shooting stick.

But all eyes fell on the dashing young Prince of Wales as he led his gleaming stallion, Kagan's Folly III, from the stable to the Royal Enclosure.

And none watched him with more hope or more concern than the beautiful full-bosomed girl who would one day become the Queen of England – Diana Spencer.

Was it really happening to her? Was it only a few weeks ago that she was teaching small children how to ride a see-saw at the Pimlico Kindergarten for Young Gentlefolk?

And then that magical evening when the Prince, gayer than she had ever seen him before, went down on one knee and begged for her hand in marriage.

She had said yes, of course, as all the world now knew. But in her heart there still remained a tiny sanctuary of doubt.

'Don't be foolish, girl,' she could hear her stepmother Raine trying to reassure her. 'Think of all his achievements – submarine commander, helicopter pilot, free-fall parachutist – why, the young Prince is a veritable Renaissance man.'

Lady Diana had listened patiently as her stepmother outlined the Prince's many virtues.

It was pointless to argue. Her stepmother would not understand that she knew dozens of men who could do these things – if not as well, then better.

She was a simple girl, a girl of the fields and meadows. What she admired in a man was the way he rode a horse, the way he deported himself on the hunting field.

No one knew this better than the Prince of Wales himself. He sensed that nothing would impress his young bride-to-be so much as to ride the winner of the coveted Lord Whelks trophy.

Now as he mounted Kagan's Folly and adjusted the flangle-strap with an expert hand, his gaze fell on the demure pale blonde beauty and he blew her a kiss.

'Good luck, Sir!' she cried, her eyes sparkling with expectation as the jockeys cantered away down Hayman's Gallop towards the starting post.

The stewards guided the horses towards the tape, and Charles could overhear the uncharitable remarks of the corps of hardened professional jockeys as they settled down for the off.

'Bleedin' toff!' muttered the familiar figure of Lester Callan, the champion jockey. 'Who does he fink he is?'

But Charles had no time to feel resentment. With a shrill cry of 'They're off!' from the crowd, the field was away and a hundred hooves were thundering down the gallop towards the first jump.

Now he felt his heart pounding with excitement. There were horses each side of him and, a long way ahead, Lester Callan was already leaping the first fence.

In his mind's eye there loomed before him the face of his beloved, her eyes imploring him to succeed, to prove to her that he was worthy of her love.

He dug his heels into the stallion's flanks. 'Come on! Come on!' he urged, and the great horse sped on towards the jump that grew ever larger in his field of vision.

This is it! he said to himself. And suddenly horse and man were airborne.

But the cheers of the crowd were short-lived. With a cry of despair the future King of England fell from the saddle and landed gracelessly on the turf, like a half-dead pheasant.

As he lay there in a daze he felt sure he could hear the uncouth cackle of the jockeys as they sped away towards the winning post . . .

♕ *Chapter 10* ♕

In which the bride-to-be finds some relationships exacting.
'She felt herself becoming woven ever deeper into the rich warp of the Royal heritage . . .'

IT WAS a cold windy morning in early April. Beneath the window of Clarence House where she stood wistfully gazing, Diana could see the brilliant red tunics of the Royal Household Fusiliers as they marched ceremoniously down the Mall towards Buckingham Palace.

Ever since she had taken up residence with Her Royal Majesty The Queen Mother, Diana had daily watched the scene and as she did so felt herself becoming woven ever deeper into the rich warp of the Royal heritage.

Every day there was something new. And there was the daily attendance at Lady Olga Maitland's School of Royal Etiquette. How difficult it was to wave and smile simultaneously! Dear Lady Olga was patience itself, but Diana still found it a struggle to master the difficult movements.

In the distance, through the misty rain, Big Ben struck eleven. It was time for coffee and biscuits in the Duke of Gloucester Room.

She found Charles's grandmother seated as always by the fire in a comfortable chintz-covered armchair, the silver tray laid out before her.

'Good morning, my dear,' said the old lady with the smile that had charmed the nation for over eighty years. 'I hope you slept well. Please help yourself to coffee.'

Diana crossed the room and arranged herself on a pile of cushions on the floor. She noticed how the Queen Mother always took her coffee in what she called the Scottish manner, by adding a 'wee nip' of finest Auld Glenkeswick Highland Cream.

It was then that the phone rang.

'Be a dear and answer it,' said the old lady, deftly replacing the cork.

Diana knew before she lifted the receiver who it would be. Not a day had gone past without her stepmother telephoning, and every day it was the same story:

'Darling, is that you? Mumsy and I are motoring up to London to have our legs waxed at Fortnum's. Perhaps we could drop in on the way home. George has shot some ducks which he specially wanted the Queen Mother to have, and Mumsy has a signed copy of this week's novel to present to her. Are you there, child? Are you listening?'

'Yes, Raine.' Diana spoke with a heavy heart.

'Let me speak to the Queen Mother,' she said.

Lady Diana explained in a whisper the position, and to her delight the old lady gave a knowing wink.

'Say we have to go and launch a new aircraft carrier,' she said with a roguish grin.

Lady Diana did as she was told. But there was no dissuading her indefatigable stepmother.

'Then we shall come tomorrow,' she said. 'I have to bring George up to see the Harley Street specialist about his back. We shall be there at four.'

So saying, Lady Raine Spencer replaced the receiver.

♛　　　♛　　　♛

The comfortable Rolls-Royce glided effortlessly along the motorway, bearing the Queen Mother and Diana towards Heathrow Airport where they had arranged to bid Charles farewell before he flew off to Australia.

'Don't upset yourself, my child,' said the kindly old lady, placing a reassuring hand on her arm. 'Five weeks will soon go by.'

Diana felt comforted by the presence of the Nation's grandmother. They had grown increasingly close in the past few weeks.

They had so much in common. Both were simple country girls who had been catapulted, much to their surprise, into the hurly-burly of Royal life.

And what a welcome change she found the Queen Mother after her years with the painted old virago of Althorp – Dame Barbara Cartland!

She shuddered involuntarily at the thought of the hideous beldame sprawled out in her feather boa, shovelling spoonfuls of yoghurt into her gaping mouth.

How the Dame had sulked when she was told that her old wedding dress, carefully preserved since 1903, would not be wanted at St Paul's!

At last the sleek black limousine swept on to the portico and the Air Minister ushered them into the VIP Lounge where Charles was waiting – looking surprisingly relaxed, Diana thought, despite the separation that lay ahead.

They scarcely had time to say a fond and fleeting farewell before the Qantas air hostess, a ravishing redhead with a deep suntan, whisked Charles towards the waiting Boeing.

Diana wandered out onto the Spectators' Balcony and the last glimpse she had of her husband-to-be was of him standing at the top of the steps waving perfunctorily in her direction while the Qantas siren took his arm and led him beguilingly into the plane.

Brushing a tear from her eye, Diana turned back into the VIP Lounge, only to be regaled by a familiar voice.

'Darling! What a wonderful surprise! Fancy seeing you here! I just happened to be passing through.'

Before Diana could utter a word of protest, Lady Spencer was beckoning the press photographers into the VIP Lounge.

'We're all here!' she cried. 'The Queen Mother and everyone!'

The sound of the jet taking off was scarcely heard above the clicking of the cameras.

♛ *Chapter 11* ♛

In which two families meet.
   'For months she had been dreading this occasion, knowing that Charles would not be there to lend support . . .'

'IN PART TWO. Botham – another duck. The Space Shuttle – more problems with the computer. And in New Zealand Prince Charles gets a right royal Maori welcome!'

Lady Diana arranged herself expectantly on the settee and waited for the adverts to come to an end.

It was Saturday evening at Althorp. She felt pleased to be home again after her long confinement at Clarence House. By the fire sat the familiar figure of her father, his loud snores filling the room as they had done ever since she could remember. Raine and her mother had gone to bed early. Indeed, they had been strangely absent throughout the day. No doubt, Diana thought, they were busy with their endless wedding plans.

At last the moment had come for her nightly glimpse of her husband-to-be. He had promised to phone her every night at eight. But obviously that was not always possible with his crowded schedule.

'And there were more surprises for His Royal Highness Prince Charles when he visited the Maori settlement of Mugga-Mugga and watched a display of gorgeous young native dancers who greeted him in the traditional way . . .'

And suddenly, on the little screen, there he was – clearly enjoying himself – strolling in that familiar way he had, one arm tucked informally into a side pocket, his head to one side, stopping to chat with one of the bare-breasted dancers.

What was he saying to her, she wondered? She could not tell. Whatever it was caused the half-naked Maori beauty to burst into peals of uninhibited laughter.

Lady Diana felt the blood rush to her cheeks. She had never thought of herself as a jealous girl but now with the Prince thousands of miles away she could not but feel left out of things. Surely her place should rightfully have been there at his side?

Her father woke up with a start. 'Eh, what?' he cried. Then he looked at his watch.

'One more nightcap and then Bedfordshire,' he said. 'Don't forget, darling, the Royals are coming over from Sandringham for lunch tomorrow. We'd better be on our best behaviour, what?'

*I*t was going much better than Diana had dared hope. For months she had been dreading this occasion, knowing that Charles would not be there to lend support.

Now here they all were, seated around the Althorp luncheon table in an atmosphere of relaxed informality.

To her surprise, Charles's father had hit it off from the start with her step-grandmother Dame Barbara Cartland. They had a mutual friend, she discovered, in the late Earl Mountbatten, and throughout luncheon had regaled one another with raucous tales of the old sea-dog's strange ways.

And there, on the other side of the table, Her Majesty The Queen had become almost animated as she discussed the training of gun-dogs with the old Earl, himself an expert on the subject.

And between the two pairs of eager conversationalists hovered her stepmother Raine, as ever the perfect hostess, filling each awkward pause with a pointful anecdote from her life at the GLC.

It was hard to believe that two such different families should be getting along so splendidly!

'Coffee in the garden!' announced Dame Barbara, rising from her seat with a flourish of her famous feather boa.

'Eh?' The old Earl looked perplexed. For this was indeed a departure from the time-honoured Althorp tradition of coffee and After Eight mints in the Duke of Wellington Room.

The party rose and hesitantly followed the stately Dame and her retinue of yapping Pekinese through the French window and out into the sunny spring garden.

Diana too was puzzled by the new departure but as she rounded the corner of the old yew hedge it all became abundantly clear.

For there, parked in the middle of the lawn, stood a gleaming silver charabanc. On its side in huge letters she read: 'Dame Barbara Cartland invites you to meet the Queen of England – $3,000 Fully Inc.'

Before the Royal Party could gather their wits and beat a retreat they were engulfed by a hysterical mob of vulgarly attired American tourists, brandishing cameras of every shape and size and asking Her Majesty to 'Smile please – for the folks back home in Atlanta, Georgia'.

How Diana wished that her betrothed was there to rescue her from this terrible nightmare.

♛ *Chapter 12* ♛

In which absence makes the heart grow fonder.
   'Diana felt a stab of excitement. Any minute now Charles's plane would be arriving at Heathrow from Washington . . .'

THE CLOCK on the kitchen wall at Clarence House struck seven and Diana felt a stab of excitement. Any minute now Charles's plane would be arriving at Heathrow from Washington and he had promised to come straight to Clarence House for a celebration reunion supper. They had arranged it before he left.

Tactful as ever, the Queen Mother had arranged to go out to the cinema for the evening. 'Have the run of the house, my dear,' she had said with her radiant smile. '*Popeye* is on at the Odeon, Leicester Square. I know I shall enjoy it. Don't wait up for me.'

So now Diana stood in the huge cavernous kitchen. All seventy-eight kitchen staff had been given the night off, and Diana felt suddenly alone as she sliced the avocado pears nervously.

It would be the first time she had prepared supper for the future King of England. Indeed, it was the first time they had ever dined alone.

She poured out the vinaigrette, carried the steaming hot pears into the dining room, and lit the candles which sparkled on the priceless silver cutlery.

How cosy it all seemed. Soon the man she loved would be there, in the candlelit room, and they would be laughing together over the stories of his travels.

Forgotten would be the empty weeks of waiting, her feuding step-parents, the fearsome figure of Dame Barbara Cartland for whom she could never feel in her heart the remotest affection.

And was all this really true? she asked herself as she surveyed the suits of armour, the Annigoni portrait of Princess Margaret and Roddy Llewellyn.

And what of her love for Charles? Was all that a dream? Strange now it seemed, but in those early days she had almost resented their forced intimacy – his hot wandering hands, his crude schoolboy jokes and jarring nautical laugh.

How everything had changed! It was surely true what the poets had said: absence makes the heart grow fonder.

Ever since he had waved goodbye to her at the airport, she had felt her love burgeon like May blossom bursting out into the sunlight.

At last she knew the meaning of true love. Before it had been a trivial affair. Now it was an overpowering emotion.

Lady Diana looked at her watch. He was on his way. She unpinned her apron and, walking through to the kitchen, pressed the switch on the microwave as the Queen Mother had shown her.

♛   ♛   ♛

*T*he kitchen clock struck half-past nine, and the black smoke from the microwave was becoming more ominous with every minute.

What could have happened? Diana was mystified. Had he fallen off something again? Her heart raced as a thousand calamities flashed through her mind.

Then at last the sharp ring of the silver telephone in the hall broke her reverie.

'Yes,' she said, desperately trying to conceal her anxiety. 'Clarence House. Who is this?'

'Pipe down, you chaps. I'm talking on the phone.'

It was his voice all right.

'I say, is that you?' His voice was scarcely audible above what sounded like a disco party in full swing.

'Held up, old girl, at the airport. This go-slow nonsense by the Customs men.'

His voice sounded slurred. No doubt it was the effects of jet-lag, she thought.

'What time shall I expect you?' she asked boldly.

'That's the point,' he replied. 'The way things are I could be here all night.' She heard renewed laughter in the background.

'Tell you what! I'll give you a tinkle on the morrow. Love to Gran. Bye!'

And with that he was gone.

Numb with disappointment, Diana opened the microwave and, taking out the burning cinders, threw them into the sink, where, like her dreams, they lay smouldering.

Chapter 13

In which news from Abroad is ill-received.
' "Don't you believe me?" he asked impatiently . . .'

'Hullo, Mummy? Can you hear me? The line's not terribly good.'
'Australia's a long way away, Charles. It never is a good line. Please speak
up!'

'O K, Mater! How's Major Bloodnok?'

'Your father's very well. How are you coping with those frightful Australians?'

'Oh God! Don't ask me that! I had to have dinner with the P M and his wife last
night. All he could talk about was his new car. And d'you know, Mummy, they served
lager. Apparently he'd never drunk anything else in his life.'

'You don't have to tell me, Charles. My heart always sinks whenever your father
suggests we go there.'

'By the way, Mater, you're not serious about me being boss out here? Surely just
your little jokey-o?'

'It wasn't my idea, Charles. It's just that you'll have to do something eventually,
after you're married.'

'Yes, I know, Mater, but not that. You know what they call Australia, don't you?
The arsehole of the Universe!'

'Really, Charles! You sound more like your father every day. And I do wish you
wouldn't use that sort of language over the phone. You never know who might be
listening in.'

'Ha ha ha!'

'Talking of your marriage, have you rung that gel of yours? I've had the Dartmouth
woman on again . . . '

'Groan!'

'. . . please don't interrupt! She really is the most dreadful creature! It's a wonder
Diana isn't more soft than she is.'

'She's not so much soft, Mater. Just a little slow. But she is still very young.'

'I know, Charles. But I do sometimes wonder if she's going to be up to it all. I mean,
what about that dress she wore to the opera?'

'Bit of all right, eh what, Mater? Plenty out front!'

'I don't know what you mean, Charles. But you'd better give her a ring, otherwise I
know perfectly well the Cartland monster will use it as an opportunity to come round
here. You know what happened when she came last?'

'No. Give me a laugh!'

'It was no laughing matter. One of her awful little Pekinese attacked poor Maurice, who was simply lying by the fire like he always does, sucking his Bonio. Before I knew what had happened, all the dogs were at each other's throats and Wheatcroft had to come and pour water on them. And d'you know what? She said it was all Maurice's fault and that Corgis were always aggressive. Charles? Are you there? What's that funny clicking noise?'

'My false teeth, Mater!'

'Charles, do be serious! I'm sure I heard a funny clicking.'

'Probably one of the abos has got his boomerang caught in the telephone wires . . .'

*L*ady Diana's hands trembled as she closed the pages of the *New York Post* and sat motionless, trying to comprehend what she had just read.

No wonder Her Majesty had been so outraged when this clearly fictitious

conversation between her husband-to-be and his mother had first been published in Germany.

No wonder that the Lord Chamberlain had immediately been instructed to apply for a writ of *scandalum magnatum*, ordering that not a word of it could ever be published in Great Britain!

But here it was, a blight on their blissfully happy reunion at Balmoral.

Charles put his arm comfortingly around her shoulder.

'Never mind, darling,' he said. 'You get a lot of that sort of thing, being royal. You just have to learn to live with it. The thing is so obviously bogus it's laughable.'

Oh, how she wanted to believe him! To be assured that her future husband could never talk so callously, so insensitively. About her. About everything.

Over the months, she thought she had seen him mellow. The Queen, too, she felt, had come to accept her as one of the family. And now this.

She got up suddenly from her chair and walked to the window, anxiously twiddling her handkerchief.

'Don't you believe me?' he asked impatiently. 'It's obviously a hoax! I've told you it's a hoax!'

Diana stared out at the rolling expanse of purple heather. She was numb.

'Surely you realize I could never possibly have said those things. God, Diana, you can be bloody thick when you want to be!'

And then suddenly a cloud drifted across the face of the sun, and the room went cold and dark.

👑 *Chapter 14* 👑

In which insult is added to injury.
'*Diana walked to the window and gazed out at the rolling parkland. Was it too late, even now, to change things – to end what was becoming daily more and more like a painful charade?*'

LADY RAINE Spencer drew back the heavy brocade curtain of her mother's bedroom and let the early morning sun stream in.

Then she carried the silver breakfast tray with its precious burden of vitamin

pills, ginseng tablets and Bulgarian yoghurt and placed it on her mother's silk counterpane.

'Wakey, wakey, mumsy darling!' she cried cheerfully, planting a kiss on her mother's frilly eye-pads.

The old beldame stirred.

'I am awake,' she said huskily, ' and have been all night.'

'Oh, mumsy,' Raine replied, 'you're not still letting yourself be disturbed by that horrid invitation, making you sit at the back. I've told you a hundred times, it was all a mistake. Diana will see to it that it's put right.'

The world-famous romantic novelist heaved herself up against the pink padded headboard, removed the lace from her eyes, and at once began to shovel vitamin pills into her mouth.

'Of course I'm not worried, Raine,' she snapped between mouthfuls. 'I've quite put it from my mind. The truth is that I had no intention of going in the first place.'

Raine stared at her mother incredulously.

'You can't mean it, mumsy. It wouldn't be a wedding without you!'

'Nonsense, child!' retorted the Dame, pouring her yoghurt into a priceless Delft bowl. 'You and I know perfectly well that the card was a prank organized by the Duke of Edinburgh, who has never liked me. Westminster Abbey, indeed! I may be eighty, but I'm not yet senile – nor ever will be, thanks to these.'

So saying, she unscrewed a phial of Megavits and thrust a handful into her mouth, crunching them vigorously with her dentures.

👑 👑 👑

*I*n the morning room on the other side of the house Diana sat, idly leafing through *The Barbara Cartland Book of Etiquette for Married Women.*

But her mind was elsewhere. How strange her home seemed now. If indeed it was her home. Had she any home? Who *was* she, she found herself frequently asking.

Yes, soon she would become a member of the Royal Family. But here at Althorp she felt caught in a no-man's-land, torn between conflicting family loyalties.

'Ah, there you are darling!' cried Raine, walking briskly into the room, a folder of papers under her arm with the word 'Wedding' typed efficiently on a little label.

'I have a tiny task for you, Diana. Mumsy is very upset. In fact, she's positively distraught about the shabby way the Palace have treated her over the invitation.'

Diana sighed and put down the book.

'I do wish you wouldn't sigh in that manner. Now listen to me, child. You're to speak to Charles and tell him that mumsy is to sit at the front along with me and your father. It's the simplest thing in the world, and the very least you can do for mumsy.'

Diana's heart felt heavy. She had no wish to undertake this awkward mission. Her days were full enough, what with visits here, there and everywhere.

'Are you listening, Diana?' Raine persisted. 'If it wasn't for mumsy I very much doubt if you would ever have met Charles. It was only because she was so friendly with Lord Mountbatten that he came here in the first place.'

Diana felt too weary to argue.

'Oh, very well, Raine,' she said. 'I'll ask Charles.'

Raine Dartmouth smiled triumphantly.

'Humph!' she snorted. 'Just see that you do!'

*N*o sooner had her mother left the room than Diana heard the slow footsteps of her father.

Then the door opened and the room was suddenly filled with bounding black labradors.

'Out, out!' cried the Earl. 'Monty, off that sofa at once!'

Obediently the dogs ran out, while the Earl hurriedly closed the door behind them.

'Little devils!' he chuckled, walking to the sideboard and pouring himself a stiff scotch.

The Earl took his drink and sat down beside his daughter, patting her affectionately on the knee.

'Just the person I want to see!' he said. 'Now then!' He cleared his throat nervously, as he always did when he had something on his mind.

'Who wants to help their dear old daddy out of a tight spot, what?'

Diana turned to face him. What could he be wanting?

'It's like this,' he began. 'Had a call from the Duke of Edinburgh last night. Awfully nice chap. I like him more and more, you know.'

'Daddy, please come to the point,' said Diana.

The old Earl took a swig from his crystal goblet.

'I've got my marching orders for the wedding. They want your mother – I mean your real mother – up front with me. As if, you know, nothing had happened.'

Diana couldn't believe it was happening to her. But she had an inkling of what was coming.

'You see how bloody awkward that's going to be,' he persevered, his face getting redder with every word. 'In a nutshell – they want Raine to sit at the back, with her mother and all the gamekeepers from the estate.'

He stood up and, walking smartly to the sideboard, replenished his glass.

'What I thought was, Diana . . .'

She cut him short.

'I know, Daddy. You want me to break the news to Raine.'

'Spot on. Good girl. Got it in one. It'll come much better from you. After all, you're practically one of *them* now.'

He paused and downed his tumbler at a single gulp.

'She never listens to me. Not any more.'

He opened the door and whistled up his faithful dogs.

'Come along now, boys and girls! Walkies!' he cried. The relief in his voice was unmistakable.

Diana walked to the window and gazed out at the rolling parkland.

How simple life had been before she said yes to the future King of England!

Was it too late, even now, to change things – to end what was becoming daily more and more like a painful charade?

She put her fair-skinned hand on the telephone and stood motionless, her thoughts in turmoil.

♛ *Chapter 15* ♛

In which Lady Diana is given some good advice.
'"You can't be sure his thoughts haven't gone a-wandering . . ."'

'COME ON, darling! We mustn't keep Keswick waiting.' Dame Barbara Cartland gathered up her Pekinese and ushered Lady Diana Spencer through the front door of Althorp Hall and towards the old family limousine drawn up on the gravel outside the portico.

'Good afternoon, your ladyships,' Keswick the chauffeur chimed, touching his peaked cap and assisting the ancient Dame into the back seat where he covered her knees with a large angora rug.

Soon the Daimler Phantom with its precious cargo was speeding towards London, where Diana was due for the final fitting of her wedding gown at Monsieur André Deutsch's salon in the heart of Knightsbridge.

Diana could not understand why her step-grandmother had suddenly thrown aside her new novel, *Love at Dusk,* to accompany her to the salon where they had arranged to meet His Royal Highness the Prince of Wales. But she was not to remain long in her state of ignorance.

Leaning forward, the ancient novelist and health fanatic closed the glass partition that separated the two of them from the prying ears and foul-smelling pipe of their ancient chauffeur.

'I'm so glad to have got you alone at last, Diana,' she began, grasping her step-grandchild's perfectly formed forearm with a surprisingly vigorous grip.

Diana shuddered. She disliked physical contact of any kind. Even the way Charles held her, she recalled, sometimes made her feel uncomfortable.

'Men, my dear!' the Dame exclaimed, as if reading her thoughts. 'They are all alike, of that you may be sure.'

She paused and, opening her jewelled handbag, deftly poured out a handful of large red iron pills and began swallowing them one by one.

'I'm sure you think I'm an interfering old busybody, but I've lived a very long life and seen a lot of the world. And although you'll find this hard to believe I have your interests at heart.'

Diana shifted uncomfortably in her seat.

'Listen to me carefully, child. No matter what they tell you, you can never be sure of a man! Oh, he'll fill your ear with all kinds of nonsense. Even when you're married and you've got him sitting there good as gold with his feet up by the fire, you can't be sure that his thoughts haven't gone a-wandering!

You have to work hard to keep him. Why else do you think I am giving you as a wedding present a lifetime's supply of my own special mixture of vitamins?'

Diana let the talk flow over her head. All this chatter about the fickleness of the opposite sex! It was easy enough to imagine why men would have grown restless in the company of Dame Barbara! (And besides, what kind of suitors had she known – gigolos, philanderers, the gay Lotharios of the Stage Door? A far cry indeed from the future King of England!)

At four o'clock punctually, the car swept into the forecourt of M. Deutsch's establishment and the proprietor M. André himself, a small dapper man with a goatee beard, rushed forward to greet them.

'*Bonjour mesdames*! Ah, Dame Barbara, what a delight to see you, ever fresh and ever young!'

A Pekinese dog leapt from the Dame's lap and bit M. André sharply on the ankle.

Soon they were ensconced in the luxurious fitting room of London's most famous couturier where M. André presided over a posse of pretty young girls, all of them busy producing his famous creations.

And there was Charles waiting for them, watching the scene, as he always did, with an air of eager interest.

The couple exchanged a few words formally.

'Now you be off, young man!' cried Dame Barbara. 'You know it's unlucky for a bridegroom to see his bride in her wedding dress before the great day!'

'Och, aye, Mein Kapitan!' replied the Prince in his funny Goon Show voice, causing M. André to burst into fits of obsequious laughter. 'I'll hang about!'

It seemed an age to Diana while M. André and his pretty young assistants fluttered about her, pinning up this hem, letting down that one. And all the time Dame Barbara sat like a great eagle, clutching her Pekinese and offering everybody the benefit of her advice.

At last it was all over, and the dress, which would soon be seen by millions all over the world, was carefully put away in its cellophane box.

Bowing and scraping, M. André bade farewell to his distinguished customers.

It was only then that Diana remembered her fiancé.

'Charles, are you there?' she called. 'We're leaving! Charles!'

A strange noise came from behind a cubicle at the far end of the salon and then a muffled cry.

'You dirty rotten swine, you deaded me!'

And then the Prince, red-faced, smiling and adjusting his tie, emerged from behind the curtain.

'Charles, darling!' cried Diana, 'what on earth were you doing in that cubicle?'

'Er . . . er . . .' stuttered the Prince, 'I was just trying on some of Monsieur André's silk ties with the help of young Monique here!'

As he spoke, a demure raven-haired seamstress with gay flashing eyes stepped out, clutching an armful of multicoloured samples.

She dropped a curtsey to the Prince and hurried out of sight.

Diana turned to the beldame. The old woman gazed deep into her eyes, and there could be no mistaking the message of her expression – *What did I tell you?*

Chapter 16

In which the Prince has a last opportunity for some bachelor fun.
'In a few hours' time he would be a married man . . .'

THE DUKE of Edinburgh piloted the Royal Helicopter skilfully onto the roof of the Playboy Club in London's fashionable Mayfair. Although it was 9.30 it was still light and across the Park the sun was just setting behind the beautiful façade of Sir Basil Spence's Knightsbridge Barracks.

Charles, wearing evening dress and medals, stooped beneath the dying swirl of the chopper's blades, followed by his brother Andrew, Captain Mark Phillips and finally the Duke.

'Buck up, you boys!' barked the latter, as they walked crocodile-fashion towards the hidden trapdoor. For this was a very secret occasion – a discreetly organized 'stag party' on the eve of the wedding of the century.

At the foot of the ladder the bearded figure of the famous radio personality and Playboy director Clement Freud was waiting to receive them, an unctuous smile playing around his whiskery lips.

'So pleased to see you, Your Highness,' he greased, bowing low and rubbing his hands like some seraglio attendant of old.

'I hope there's been no bloody leaks!' rasped the Duke, as Freud ushered them into the darkened recesses of the Hefner Suite where a posse of gorgeous Bunny Girls was waiting to greet the Royal Party with trays of drinks and bowls of Twiglets.

The guests were already assembled. Harvey Smith, hero of a thousand horse trials, leaned over the roulette table, a large vodka in one hand, a pile of chips in the other. Anthony Holden, Charles's young biographer, listened intently to the ebullient Harry Secombe who, as he munched a portion of Colonel Sanders' delicious Fried Chicken, regaled the youthful man of letters with many a colourful tale of his barefoot boyhood days on the Welsh mountainside.

Across the smoke-filled room Charles could espy his childhood idol Spike Milligan, wearing a comic nautical cap and a boiler suit. He was on the bandstand playing the piano while Chappie d'Amato, leader of the small orchestra, looked on anxiously.

'There you are, my boy,' said the Duke, 'I've sent your brother home – he's just been sick.'

Charles looked at his watch. It had gone three. In a few hours' time he would be a married man, with all the cares and responsibilities of matrimony.

The Duke seemed to read his thoughts.

'A touch of the pre-marital collywobbles, what, my boy?' he said, placing a paternal arm around his son's broad shoulder, 'Just you remember this and you'll be alright. Make certain you're the boss from the word go. That's the Golden Rule. Make the little lady pretty damned sure who wears the trousers. Then you won't get any trouble.'

Charles was touched. His father had never spoken to him with such tenderness before.

And his advice, he felt sure, was worth heeding.

'Take your mother and me,' the Duke went on. But for a moment his eye was caught by a voluptuous Bunny Girl as she danced exotically to the former Goon's slumbrous rhythms.

'I put my foot down on Day 1. I said to her, "You may be Queen of England one day, my dear, but as far as I'm concerned, you're the Little Woman . . ."'

Alas, the Duke's words were drowned as the piercing tenor of Harry Secombe led the glittering assembly in a rousing chorus of that fine old Scottish air, 'Four and twenty ladies came down frae Inverness . . .'

👑   👑   👑

Dawn was already breaking as father, son and son-in-law tiptoed up the Marble Staircase of Buckingham Palace. The long hours of revelry had certainly taken their toll on the Royal merrymakers.

Captain Mark Phillips stumbled as he began the ascent and let out a soldierly oath.

'Quiet you fool!' snapped the Duke. 'You'll wake the whole bloody household!'

As he spoke, the majestic figure of the Queen of England, wearing a long night-robe, appeared at the top of the stairs, striking awe into the hearts of the three men.

'Philip!' she began in icy tones. 'And what do you think you're doing? Have you any idea what the time is?'

Her husband shook his head sheepishly.

'I told you all you were to be back by twelve at the latest. We have a very long and, need I emphasize, important day ahead of us.'

There was a crash as Captain Phillips fell backwards and collapsed at the foot of the stairs.

'Carry him up to his room,' said the Queen, 'and I want to see you both properly spruced up in the Morning Room at seven-thirty sharp.'

And with that she turned on her heel and swept upstairs.

The Duke looked at his son, a woebegone expression in his eyes.

'Who'd be bloody married!' he muttered. 'Whoops, sorry!'

Big Ben struck the hour. It sounded to Charles like the tolling of a passing age.

♛ *Chapter 17* ♛

In which an Intruder shatters an idyll.
'The canopy of the Beaton bed was ripped asunder . . .'

LADY DIANA Windsor strolled on to the promenade deck of *H.M.S. Britannia* and gazed out over the sleepy tropical lagoon to where the lights of Santa del Monico twinkled under the velvet canopy of stars.

In the cool sea breeze she wrapped her silken shawl, a present from the Queen, round her perfectly formed shoulders and sighed with contentment.

At last it was all over and she and Charles were alone. Away, away from the madding crowd – the flag-waving well-wishers, the friends and relations, and above all, away from the prying prurient eyes of the journalists and the photographers.

From the beginning they had invaded her world like a plague of hungry locusts, feasting on every little morsel they could find. Diana had learned even to recognize some of them by sight – Whitaker with his binoculars, Dempster, a cruel heart beneath the sophisticated veneer, and the most despised of all – McKay, the ubiquitous Scotsman who seemed to know their every secret move.

But now they were all a long way away, separated from them by thousands of miles of ocean!

'Happy, darling?'

As if reading her thoughts Charles stood beside her, wearing his Admiral of the Fleet uniform and puffing at a Meerschaum pipe.

She snuggled up to him against the handrail and linked arms.

'Blissfully, darling,' she replied. 'And you?'

Charles looked at his watch.

'It's getting late,' he said, yawning. 'It's been a long day.'

Above them on the foc's'le a group of cheerful sailors struck up a gay sea-shanty. 'Oh ho, ho! It's a sailor's life for me,' they sang with merry abandon.

Charles tapped his pipe in time with the rollicking melody. She had never seen him so relaxed.

'Tired?' he asked, placing his arm around her waist.

'A little,' she said, looking with disbelief at the sapphire- and emerald-encrusted band of gold on her finger. Was it only that morning that the kindly old Archbishop Runcieballs had asked her if she would 'love, cherish and obey'?

Oh, she would, she would!

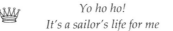

Yo ho ho!
It's a sailor's life for me

The voices of the crew were still audible from the deck above as Diana stood in the Queen Mary Suite of the *Britannia* and gazed about her with awe.

The exquisitely furnished room was filled with bouquets of sweet-smelling flowers and fragrant with the scents of exotic pot-pourri. Soft lights caressed the deep Persian rugs and the fine mellow wood of the Chippendale commodes.

And there in the centre of the suite was the famous Cecil Beaton four-poster bed, a voluptuous masterpiece of quilted satin and ormolu, designed by the great *Maître de Boudoir* at the very height of his powers.

She felt the gentle swaying of the boat and heard the purr of the engines throbbing quietly beneath.

And then suddenly Charles turned and took her in his arms. She felt his hot breath on her soft cheeks and his strong manly arms pulling her towards him in a passionate embrace. Her head spun! What was happening to her? A mixture of fear and ecstasy swept her away on a tide of romantic bliss.

'Good luck, Your Royal Highness!'

Suddenly a familiar Scottish voice shattered their idyll. And then with a terrible rending of priceless Venetian silks, the canopy of the Beaton bed was ripped asunder and the diminutive body of the journalist McKay crashed onto the bed, his cameras and lenses bouncing around his burly form.

Diana stared in astonishment and dismay at his unconscious form lying in her husband's place, an empty hipflask clutched in his red paw-like hand.

Above, the choir of matelots sang on – like demons in a nightmare . . .

Ho, ho ho!
It's a sailor's life for me!

The End